Pet... ...lway
A ... of Energy

by
Christopher Vine

The watercolour illustrations are by John Wardle

Published by
Christopher Vine 2011

Printed by The Amadeus Press
Copyright © 2011 Christopher Vine

ISBN 978-0-9553359-7-6

The Peter's Railway Series

Peter and his Grandpa have built an amazing miniature steam railway between their houses; Woodland Cottage and Crossacres Farm. The line even runs to Yockletts Village where Peter goes to school.

The locomotive, Fiery Fox, is a wonderful machine. Bright green and very powerful.

Apart from the pleasure of building the railway and other projects, Peter has loved learning so much about science and engineering.

Grandpa always takes the time to answer questions, however tricky they may be.....

A Bit of Energy

One afternoon, Peter and Grandpa were having a steam up on their railway. They had invited some friends over for the day.

It was a great pleasure to see the farm and countryside rolling by from the little train. And at Yewston station, they had one of Grandma's world famous tea and cake parties!

The locomotive, Fiery Fox, had driven quite a few miles as they travelled up and down. She had hauled the heavy train with untiring energy: Stopping, starting, fast, slow, up and down the gradients on the line.

The friends were all amazed how such a small machine could do so much work.

They had enjoyed a wonderful afternoon, seen many sights, travelled lots of miles and eaten too many cakes. But now it was time to put the train away.

Grandpa let the fire down while Peter polished all the paint and metal on the locomotive.

Cara, one of Peter's friends, was watching everything with interest, but something was puzzling her.

"Peter," she asked when he had finished, "where does all the energy come from, that makes Fiery Fox work so hard?"

"That's a good question," replied Peter looking up. "I'll try to explain, but I'm sure Grandpa will help if I get stuck."

"The secret is in Fiery Fox's tender," Peter began. "All the energy for all the work she does is contained in the coal."

Cara picked up a small lump and looked at it more carefully. "What, this stuff?" she said. "This black stone doesn't look like it could do anything at all!"

"That's the wonder of a steam engine," laughed Peter. "It takes a simple thing like coal and converts it into something really useful, like pulling a train.

"The amount of energy in that one lump you are holding is incredible," he continued. "That single lump of coal could boil a whole kettleful of water."

Peter explained that the first thing the steam engine had to do, was convert the energy in the coal into a form of energy which it could use.

"When you put coal in the firebox and burn it, you are changing all the chemical energy in the coal into heat energy.

"Huge amounts of heat and scorching hot flames," he continued. "And do you know what the boiler does with all that heat?"

"Yes, it turns it into steam," answered Cara.

"Exactly," agreed Peter. "The boiler takes the heat from the coal fire and uses it to boil water and make hot steam at high pressure. The energy in the steam can then be used to drive the locomotive."

"The next bit of magic takes place in the cylinders," said Grandpa, taking up the story and pointing to the front of the engine.

"It is the pistons and cylinders which take the energy in the steam and change it into useful mechanical effort to pull the train," he explained.

"They don't look much from the outside, but inside is something very cunning."

Grandpa explained that the round piston is a perfect sliding fit in its cylinder. It can slide backwards and forwards, but fits so well that the steam cannot leak past it.

When one end of the cylinder is filled with high pressure steam, it pushes very hard on the piston.

"Pistons are a bit like the muscles in your legs, pushing on the pedals of your bicycle. But in an engine the pistons push on the cranks to turn the wheels.

"Because the steam is at high pressure, it pushes on the piston with an incredible force.

"In Fiery Fox the pistons are quite small, only 6 centimetres across, but the pressure of the steam pushes with a force the same as the weight of 3 adult men.

"In the full size engine, the piston is 50 centimetres diameter and the steam pushes with a force of more than 30 tonnes. That is the weight of a large lorry, or eight elephants!" laughed Grandpa.

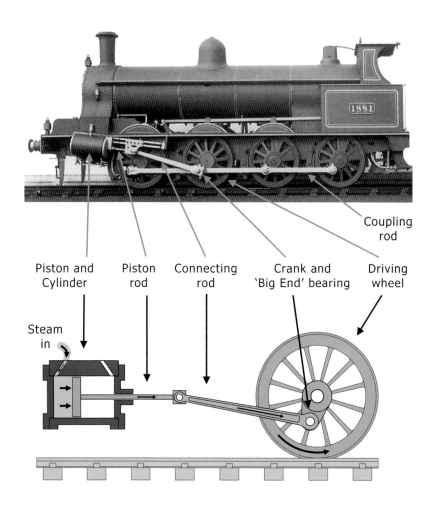

Coupling rod

Piston and Cylinder

Piston rod

Connecting rod

Crank and 'Big End' bearing

Driving wheel

Steam in

Now it was Peter's turn to be puzzled. "But where does the energy in the coal come from?" he asked.

"Now that is another good question," laughed Grandpa, "and I think the answer will surprise you.

"Do you remember the time you looked into the firebox and said it was like looking at the Sun? Well in a way you were right. All the energy in the coal came from the Sun," he explained, pointing to the sky.

"Although it doesn't look like it, coal is made from trees or plants which grew millions of years ago. In fact the coal we were burning in Fiery Fox today, probably came from trees which were alive even before the dinosaurs walked the earth."

Grandpa explained that there is a huge amount of energy in sunlight. "You know it's there because, on a sunny day, you can feel it as heat on your face.

"Trees are very good at collecting that energy. Their leaves convert it into food so that the tree can create wood to make the trunk and branches grow.

"If you burn a piece of wood, it gives the Sun's energy back as heat from the flames. The longer the tree lives, the larger it gets and the more sunlight energy it stores in its wood."

"But how does the tree end up as coal?" Peter wanted to know.

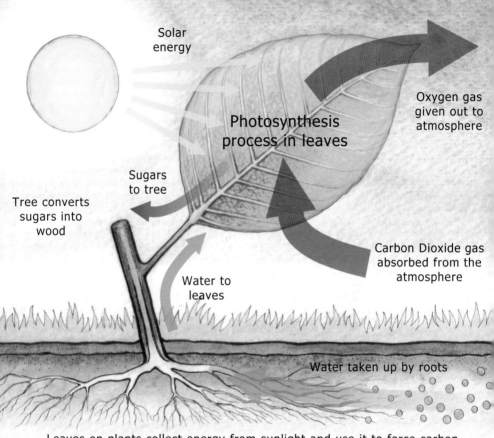

Solar energy

Photosynthesis process in leaves

Oxygen gas given out to atmosphere

Sugars to tree

Tree converts sugars into wood

Carbon Dioxide gas absorbed from the atmosphere

Water to leaves

Water taken up by roots

Leaves on plants collect energy from sunlight and use it to force carbon dioxide gas from the air, to combine with water to make sugars. This process is called 'photosynthesis' and is what powers all plant life on earth.

"That's the next stage," continued Grandpa, "and it takes millions and millions of years. It happened so long ago that the plants growing then were not much like our trees today. They were more like ferns.

"If they were growing in shallow water or on a boggy marsh, they would sink to the bottom when they died. The water kept the air out and prevented them rotting away to nothing.

"As time went on, their remains got buried by millions of tonnes of sediment or sand. This huge weight and higher temperature underground, turned the old plant matter into coal.

"Usually coal is buried deep underground, but sometimes you can see it at the surface.

This picture shows a seam of coal in the side of a cliff. The coal has been squashed between two different layers of rock. The top brown rock is the sediment which has settled on the dead plants.

"If the coal is near the surface, it's quite easy to get at," explained Grandpa. "The top layer of soil can be scraped away and then the coal dug out with huge machines.

"But where the coal deposits lie deep underground, long tunnels have to be dug to reach it. Sometimes the tunnels are miles long.

"In the old days, miners had to endure terrible conditions. They worked in the dark and in cramped spaces where they couldn't even stand up. They had only a candle for light and that could cause gas explosions.

"There was also the constant danger of the roof collapsing on top of them," Grandpa added grimly."

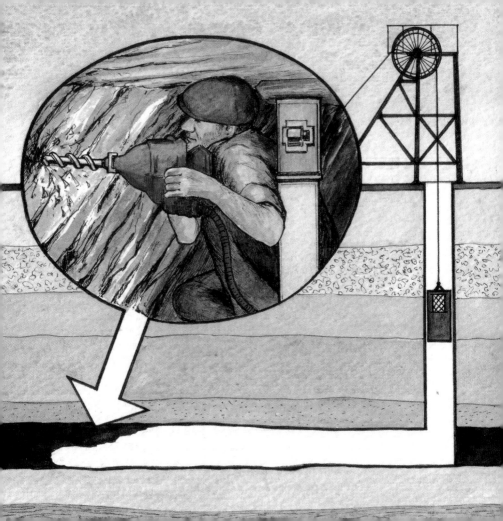

"It sounds horrible," said Peter shuddering. "But let's see if I've got this right:

"The Sun gave energy to the trees and plants millions of years ago....

"The plants grew and trapped the energy from the sunlight in their wood....

"Then the plants died and over millions of years buried underground, they turned into coal....

"The energy stored in the coal is then turned into heat energy in the engine's firebox and the heat makes steam in the boiler....

"And finally the energy in the steam drives Fiery Fox by pushing on the pistons.

Grandpa agreed, nodding.

"But Grandpa," Peter paused.............

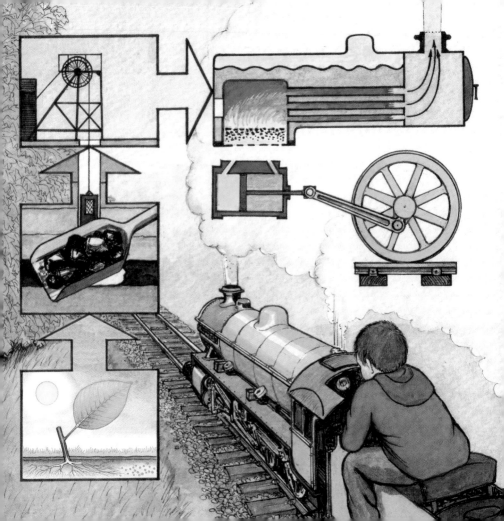

"Where does all the energy in the Sun come from?" he asked.

Poor Grandpa! He had been really proud of his explanation about energy, but this question was simply beyond him.

"It just does!" he laughed, saying what most adults say when children ask them things.

The End.

Do you know where the energy in the Sun comes from? See if you can find someone to explain it to you.

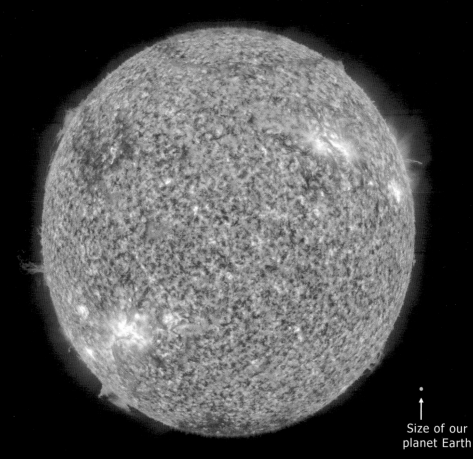

Size of our
planet Earth

The Sun's diameter is 109 times bigger than the Earth.
The flames on the left are 50,000 miles high!

Photo NASA

Why Peter's Railway?

Since a very small boy, Chris has always loved anything mechanical and especially steam engines. The first workshop was in his bedroom where he made an electric go-kart aged 8, followed by a mini-bike powered by the engine from a petrol lawn mower.

He spent many holidays on a friend's farm where there was a miniature railway across a field and so started a love of making model steam locomotives. The latest is Bongo, 8 feet long and the inspiration for Fiery Fox in the books.

Chris wanted to share his love and knowledge of railways and engineering: Peter's Railway is the result.

Story   **Technical**   **Adventure**

The original books

The original four books tell the charming story of Peter and his Grandpa building and running their steam railway across the farm. At the ends of chapters are special how-it-works pages with simple (but accurate) explanations of what has been happening in the story. In addition, Grandpa tells some wonderful stories from the old days on the railways.   Age range 6 - 12 years approx.

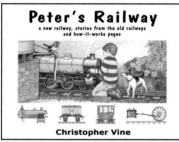

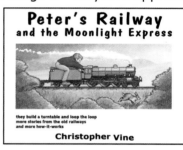

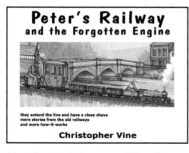

Hardback, 96 pages 17 x 24 cm with 30 watercolour pictures by John Wardle and 14 pages of clearly explained technical drawings. £11.99

New! Small format books

A new series of Peter's Railway in a smaller format. While the original books each contain several story or adventure threads, separate technical pages and Grandpa's tales, the small books concentrate on one aspect; a Peter's adventure, a Grandpa's tale of the old railways or a technical book.

'Little Peter's Railway' are gentle stories for younger children.

Little
Peter's Railway
Christmas Steam
Peter saves Christmas

Little
Peter's Railway
Surprise Goods
A bed-time story with a twist....

Peter's Railway
A Bit of Energy
Grandpa tries to answer a tricky question

Peter's Railway
A Dark and Stormy Night
Grandpa tells a tale from the old days

Paperbacks with 32 pages, 12 watercolour pictures - £2.99